My 1st CELL PHONE RULES!

By Allison B. Chan

DEDICATION

To my daughters, Lily and Zoe. May this book serve as a reminder that if you work hard and follow your passions you can make your childhood dreams a reality.
To my husband, Grant, for imagining a "Hippopotomoose".

Hippopotomoose's FIRST cell phone.

How EXCITING!

OH MY!!!

NOW it is IMPORTANT to learn the
RULES to live by.

BUT it is IMPORTANT to pay attention
WHERE you are WALKING.

CELL PHONES can be used to CALL or text FRIENDS.

Just be SURE to TALK in-person NOW and THEN.

Cell phones have a LOT
of FUN games to PLAY.

BUT don't forget to SPLISH SPLASH on a rainy DAY.

Although it can HELP with HOMEWORK, which is COOL.

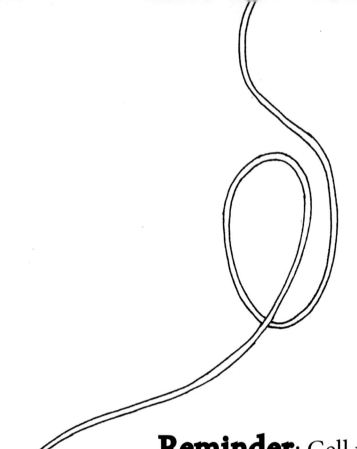

Reminder: Cell phones need to be CHARGED with POWER.

KEEP your eyes HEALTHY by NOT staring at it HOUR after HOUR.

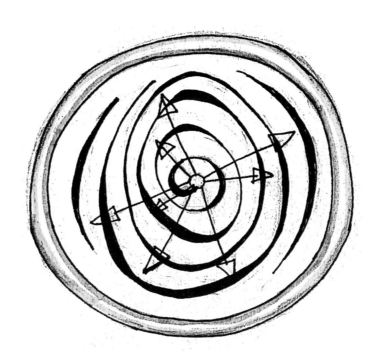

Cell phones can HELP you if you are in DANGER.

Cell phones SHOULDN'T be used during PLAYS and MOVIES, because you might miss SOMETHING that is REALLY super GROOVY.

NEVER use your cell phone to BULLY others.

Cell phones LIKE PEOPLE come in MANY SHAPES and COLORS.

Cell phones are especially RAD when YOU use them to SAY

to your MOM and your DAD.

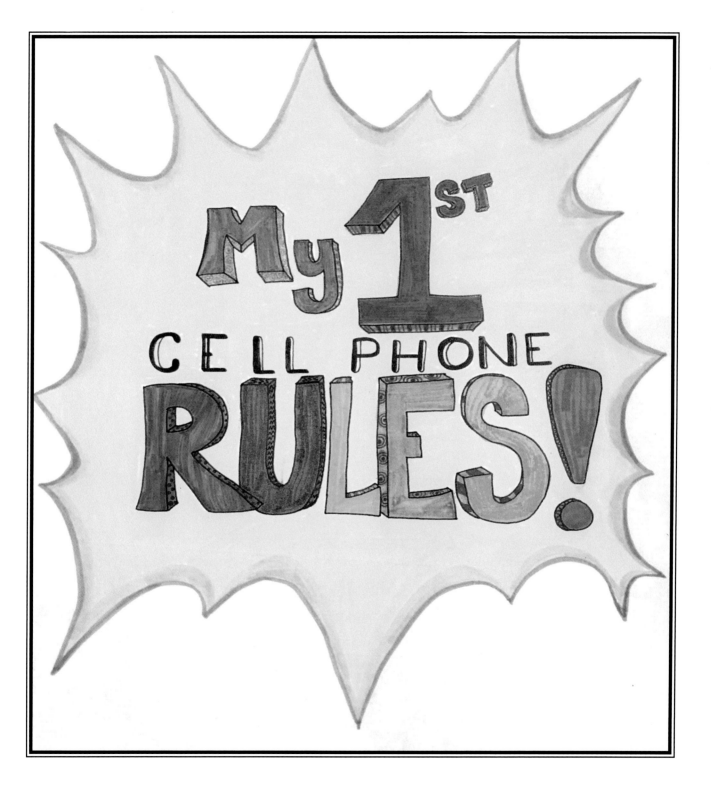

ABOUT THE AUTHOR

Allison Chan is a 3rd generation Nevada County native who received her B.A. in Art Studio from the University of California, Davis. The inspiration for this book came to her during the first date night with her husband, after the birth of their first child, where she observed people using their cell phones instead of enjoying the company of those around them. She is the mother of two beautiful, spirited and inquisitive girls. She is a caring teacher and serves on the Board of Directors of the award winning multicultural theatre company, Community Asian Theatre of the Sierra (C.A.T.S.) which promotes diversity in her hometown. She would like to thank you for sharing her first book with your own sweet hippopotomoose.

Made in the USA
Monee, IL
29 December 2020

55888965R00017